C000270215

✿ **Design** Rob Baalham   ✿ **Production Editor** Robbie Kelly
✿ **Editor** Gill Smith   ✿ Extra help from Biscuit the cat

Colour origination by Radstock Reproductions Ltd, Midsomer Norton
Printed and bound in Belgium by Proost NV, Turnhout

✿ First published in 1999 by BBC Worldwide Ltd, Woodlands, 80 Wood Lane,
London, W12 0TT ✿ *Girl Talk* copyright © BBC Worldwide Ltd 1999

All rights reserved

ISBN 0 563 55622 6

CONTENTS

4 'Jessica the TV Star' – Sweet Valley Kids special part 1

8 Hearing dogs for the deaf

10 Story – 'Back in Time'

14 Gardening puzzles

16 Pet Hotel cartoon

20 Stars of the new millennium

22 Recipes

24 Short story – 'Donkey Derby'

26 ABC quiz

28 Playtime puzzles

30 2000 year planner

32 How to draw

34 Make it! with SMart

36 Fashion through the millennium

38 Short story – 'Storm Lights'

40 Funny fluffies

42 Best Friends cartoon

46 A jumble of puzzles

48 Customise your clothes

50 'Jessica the TV Star' – Sweet Valley Kids special part 2

54 How to sponsor an animal

56 Short story – 'Nasarin's Egyptian Experience'

58 The Girl Talk bumper general knowledge quiz

THE ALL-NEW ADVENTURES OF Sweet Va

🌸 JESSICA THE TV STAR

Part 1

One morning, Elizabeth wasn't feeling very well

I think I'm ill.

Do you think you'll have to stay home from school?

Probably. Mum says that I have a fever.

I wish I could stay home, too.

Psst! Elizabeth, I need to tell you a secret at break.

Okay, Todd. I'll meet you behind the big tree.

I wonder what it can be!

Over here! I don't want anyone else to hear.

My mum and dad know a TV producer. He's going to film a programme at our house.

Really? I wish I could see a film being made.

Nothing. It's just that I want you to be in it, Elizabeth.

Todd will be really angry if he finds out I'm Jessica!

Can Jessica be in it, too?

No! And you must promise not to tell her – don't tell anyone.

Oh.

You have to come round after school tomorrow for a rehearsal. Then we film the next day.

✿ JESSICA THE TV STAR

Jessica has been pretending to be Elizabeth

Are you sure you feel well enough to go to school today?

I'm fine.

You're very pale. Maybe you should stay home.

Jessica, I'm okay.

Where are you going?

I'm going to ride my bike over to Todd's house.

Elizabeth will be home from football practice in an hour. You had better be back, too.

Don't worry.

Hi. The director's ready for the run-through.

Not you!

Sorry, I forgot.

You're acting just like Jessica.

What do you mean?

You know – bossy.

Okay, let's try it again.

See me, hear me

More than just a best friend, a hearing dog provides a helpful pair of ears to deaf or hearing-impaired people

As the saying goes, a dog is a (hu)man's best friend. This is particularly true of the specially trained dogs which provide help, security and companionship to people with disabilities. Hearing Dogs for Deaf People is a charity that improves the lives of deaf and hearing-impaired people by training dogs to alert their owners to everyday sounds, such as the doorbell or the alarm clock.

Getting on with people

This puppy is learning to socialise. This can take between two and eight months depending on the age of the puppy. The socialiser is responsible for training each dog to be obedient, friendly, confident and well-mannered. He or she gives the dog an introduction to everyday life by travelling with it on buses and trains, visiting shops and other public places. The socialiser trains the dog by rewarding good behaviour.

Pet rescue

Many hearing dogs come from rescue centres. But this puppy, Archie, was kindly donated to the charity. Archie will spend the first part of his training in the care of one of the charity's patient, hard-working, volunteer puppy socialisers. Good luck, Archie!

HEARING DOG PUPPY

It's for you!

After the socialising stage the young dog is brought to the training centre, where the sound work begins. The dog will be trained to alert its trainer to about seven or eight different sounds. This part of the training takes four months. Here, *Girl Talk* reader Jodi Lawler is in the training centre, of her favourite charity. Jodi pretends to be asleep and Pinta leaps on to the bed to let her know the alarm clock is ringing. That would get anyone out of bed in the morning!

Success

After three months in the home and care of its new owner the dog is given a final assessment in all of the four training subjects. Once it has been successful the dog's hard work is rewarded with a distinctive golden yellow jacket and a special certificate. This picture of Dexter was taken shortly after he became a fully qualified hearing dog. Well done, Dexter!

Class exams

At the training centre potential dog owners are taught how to manage and care for them. It is important that they know what to do when they have the dog in their own home. Here, Jodi is using an arm signal to ask Pinta "What is it?" Pinta is alerting her that the doorbell has rung. When the dog achieves a 75 per cent pass rate in sound work, obedience, socialisation and handling, it is allowed home with its owner.

Sponsors

It costs £2,500 to select, socialise and train each hearing dog and a further £2,500 for the placement and aftercare. But, thanks to fundraisers and companies who sponsor dogs, hearing dogs are free for deaf people. Jodi is donating a box of stamps, which will raise money to train a hearing dog. Perhaps you and your friends in school could do the same thing?

For more information about their work you can contact the charity at:
Hearing Dogs for Deaf People, London Road, Lewknor, Oxfordshire, OX9 5RY, tel (01844) 353898

❀ Words: Nora Kearns ❀ Pictures: James Jordan and Hearing Dogs for Deaf People

Back

Illustrations: Flora Daneman

The history of the school was a mystery to the girls – until the headmistress gave them the key that would unlock the past

A story by Narinder Dhami

"This is so boring!" Zoë threw her pen down in disgust and nudged her best friend, Emma, who was sitting next to her. "Why couldn't Donald Duck give us something interesting to do?"

"He did say that Mrs Walker might be able to help us," Emma pointed out, hopefully.

"Oh yes, when she gets round to it," Zoë snorted. She looked down gloomily at the large piece of paper in front of them. Their class was doing a big project about the end of the millennium and everyone had been given a different area to research. Zoë and Emma had been told to write about the preparations the school was making to celebrate the turn of the millennium and to compare it with how the school had celebrated the turn of the century in 1900, in Victorian times. But Zoë and Emma didn't know anything about what had happened in 1900.

Imagination

The headmistress, Mrs Walker, had promised to look through the old school files to see if she

could find some information for them, but so far she hadn't got round to it.

"How are you getting on, girls?" Mr Duckworth, their teacher, came over to them and frowned as he saw the empty piece of paper. "Not too well so far, I see."

"We just don't know where to start, sir," Zoë muttered dismally.

"Well, maybe you could just use your imagination," Mr Duckworth suggested, looking a bit desperate himself. "You know, try making something up."

"Oh, great!" Zoë muttered as the teacher hurried off. "Some help he was!"

"Zoë? Emma?" Right at that moment Mrs Walker popped her head round the classroom door and beckoned to them.

"I'm sorry I haven't had a chance to look at the old school documents for you," she went on as Zoë and Emma joined her. "So I thought you might like to take a look at them for yourselves. They're in the big cupboard marked Store room, right at the top of the school." She took a heavy, old-fashioned key from her pocket and handed it to Zoë.

"Thanks, Miss," Zoë said gratefully. Now at least she and Emma might be able to get something done!

"Be careful!" Mrs Walker called after them as the two girls hurried off eagerly. "No one has opened that cupboard for years – it's probably full of dust and dead spiders!"

Spooky

Zoë and Emma ran up the stairs two at a time. The school was a very old one. It had been built in 1885 and was on four floors, although the top floor wasn't used much except for storage, and it was usually out of bounds to the pupils. When the girls reached the top of the stairs,

Continued overleaf

panting, they both stopped and looked round nervously. It was very quiet up there, and very dusty, too. "This is spooky," Emma whispered in Zoë's ear as they walked over to the cupboard.

"What are you whispering for?" Zoë said with a grin. She put the key in the lock and tried to turn it. It was a little stiff, but she eventually managed it. The cupboard door swung open with a loud creak, which made both girls jump.

"Look at this!" Zoë said, her eyes wide as she stared inside.

The cupboard was so big that it was possible to walk right inside. It was crammed full of old folders and files and exercise books, all piled up higgledy-piggledy, in no particular order. Some were on the shelves and others were just lying in heaps on the floor. Everything was so dusty it all looked as though it would fall to pieces if anyone touched anything.

Emma groaned. "Look at it," she complained. "It's going to take us ages to sort through this lot!"

Zoë wasn't listening. "What's that?" she said, pointing at another door in the far wall of the cupboard.

"It looks like a door to me," Emma said sarcastically.

"Yes, but where does it go?" Zoë asked. She went over to the door, and pulled it open.

There was a sudden rush of strong wind which made both Zoë and Emma gasp with shock, followed by a blinding dazzle of sunlight, which meant that for a moment or two neither girl could see in front of them.

"There you are, girls," said a brisk voice all of a sudden. "Hurry and take your places, please."

Scared

Zoë and Emma both blinked, their eyes watering. Neither of them could believe what they were seeing. They were back in Mr Duckworth's classroom – but it wasn't Mr Duckworth's classroom. It was different. There were no tables and chairs, no colourful displays on the walls and hardly any bookcases full of books. Instead the room was crammed with rows and rows of dark wooden benches, which rose steadily higher,

like seats in a theatre. The benches were crowded with girls on one side of the room and boys on the other, and they were all dressed in very old-fashioned clothes. The girls were wearing what looked like pinafores over their dresses, and strange-looking boots with buttons. Then Zoë realised with a shock that she and Emma were dressed in exactly the same clothes, too!

"Zoë!" Emma whispered, looking scared out of her wits. "Where are we? And why are we dressed like this?"

Before Zoë could answer, the teacher standing at the front of the room rapped sharply on the wooden floor with her long cane. She was a tall, thin woman with hair scraped back into a severe bun, and gold-rimmed glasses. She wore a long black dress which swept right down to the floor. "Girls! Take your places please."

Zoë grabbed Emma's hand and pulled her onto the nearest bench. Then she noticed the blackboard. January 3rd, 1900 was written on it in white chalk.

"I think we've gone back in time!" she whispered, almost bursting with excitement.

Emma turned pale. "Stop messing about, Zoë!"

"Well, what else could have happened?" Zoë demanded breathlessly. Then she shut up quickly as the teacher gave her a stern glance.

"Let us continue with what we were doing," the teacher said, indicating a small tin box which was lying on the desk in front of her. "Please bring the objects you have decided on, and place them in the box."

"What's going on?" Emma whispered nervously to Zoë.

"I haven't got a clue!" Zoë whispered back.

Some of the children stood up and went quietly to the front of the class. Each one of them was carrying something, which

in turn they put into the tin box. There was a bundle of papers, some photographs, a large shiny silver coin and some flags, including a Union Jack. When everything had been placed inside, the teacher closed the box, and picked it up. "Now we shall go and bury it in the far left-hand corner of the field at the back of the school," she announced sternly. "Everybody stand, please."

Zoë nudged Emma. "It's a time capsule!" she gasped.

Emma wasn't listening. "Quick, let's get out of here," she whispered as all the children stood up obediently and filed out under the teacher's eagle eye. "I don't like this."

Vanished

Zoë and Emma slipped away, back to the cupboard door. As Zoë pulled it open, she wondered what would happen to them if it didn't take them back to their own time. But once again there was a surge of wind and the next moment they were back on the other side of the cupboard, and back in their own clothes again.

"We're home!" Emma said joyfully.

"That was scary!"

"Have you found anything, girls?"

The voice from the corridor outside nearly made both girls jump out of their skin. Then a second later Mrs Walker came in.

"Oh, Miss!" Emma gabbled, "You'll never guess what happened

to us! We went through that door there and…"

Emma stopped and stared. So did Zoë. The door at the back of the cupboard had completely vanished. There was only a wall there now. Mrs Walker frowned. "What door?" Luckily she didn't wait for an answer. "Well, have you found anything or not?"

"Yes, Miss, we have!" Zoë said, feeling more and more excited. "We think some of the pupils buried a time capsule in 1900 to celebrate the new century, and we know where it is!"

Mrs Walker looked interested. "Where?"

"The far left-hand corner of the sports field," Zoë said triumphantly. "We saw something about it in one of these, er, documents."

"Yes, but now we can't remember which one we found it in," Emma said, backing Zoë up.

A few moments later the headmistress, Zoë and Emma were hurrying across the sports field along with the caretaker, who was carrying a spade.

"I hope it's still there," Emma whispered to Zoë, "Or we're going to look like right wallies!"

"It will be!" Zoë said confidently.

Secret

They went to the farthest bit of the left-hand corner of the field, and the caretaker began to dig. Zoë and Emma were on tenterhooks, waiting to see what would happen. After about fifteen minutes of digging, there was a loud clink as the spade hit something metallic.

"That's it! That's it!" Zoë danced around the hole in excitement. "That's the tin box!"

The caretaker dug carefully around the box, and pulled it out. It wasn't shiny any more, and it was rather battered. Mrs Walker opened it carefully while Zoë and Emma watched intently.

"This is amazing!" Mrs Walker said. "Look, girls!" She took out the bundle of papers and photographs. "There are lots of newspaper clippings about how the school celebrated the turn of the century, and some accounts written by some of the pupils, too." She picked up the row of flags. "These

must have been what they used to decorate the school, and look at this." She handed the silver coin, now badly tarnished, to Zoë. It had an engraving of Queen Victoria on one side, and a picture of the school on the other. "I think all the children might have been given one of these coins as a souvenir."

Zoë nudged Emma. "Looks like we'll have plenty of information for our project now," she said, triumphantly.

"Yes, but no one would believe us if they knew how we had found out!" Emma whispered back, and the two girls grinned at each other.

"I think that had better be our little secret!" said Zoë. ❀

PUZZLES

Don't make any bloomers with these great gardening puzzles

Blooming lovely!

Two of these flowers are identical. Can you tell which ones?

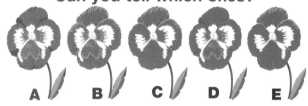

A   B   C   D   E

Answer Flowers C and E are identical.

FLOWER POWER

Rearrange the missing letters from these clues to spell out the name of a favourite flower

1 If you n_o_d your head, it means yes

2 Jack and J_i_ll went up the hill...

3 Kittens are soft and flu_ll_y

4 Monday is the day before Tues_da_y

Answer Daffodil

STRAWBERRY PICKING

How many strawberries can you count growing in the pot?

Answer There are 24 strawberries.

GREEN FINGERS

You may know where these things are in your garden, but can you find them hidden in this word square?

P	O	N	D	E	W	E	E	D	S	U	Z
M	V	E	G	E	T	A	B	L	E	S	G
H	L	O	W	P	L	A	N	T	S	V	Q
O	S	A	P	E	E	B	E	N	C	H	A
E	F	C	W	D	M	Y	V	S	D	C	H
G	A	L	A	N	L	D	F	G	R	V	O
G	K	P	O	S	M	S	H	O	S	E	I
Z	S	S	E	W	L	O	H	U	R	E	D
D	E	E	Q	Z	E	M	W	E	S	P	R
F	R	F	X	A	W	R	K	E	D	J	Z
T	S	W	I	N	G	A	S	E	R	Y	T
B	I	R	D	B	A	T	H	H	Z	W	J

SHED PLANTS POND LAWNMOWER
BIRDBATH SPADE VEGETABLES BENCH
FLOWERS SWING WEEDS HOE TREES HOSE

MESSY BEDS

The flower bed is overrun with weeds so can you work out which roots actually lead to the flowers?

A B C D E F G H I J

Answers Weeds A C G Flowers B D H

VEGETABLE PATCH

Can you identify the odd one out in this jumbled vegetable patch?

1. LE KE
2. OO NIN
3. TRC AOR
4. ATTO OM
5. TPTO AO
6. CLOC BOIR

Answers 1 Leek 2 Onion 3 Carrot 4 Tomato 5 Potato 6 Broccoli
Number 4 because a tomato is a fruit.

WRIGGLY WORD

YARD

Yarn
Warn
Warm

Can you pull a worm out of the yard by changing just one letter at a time?

WORM

Answers Yard Yarn Warn Warm Worm

PICTURE THIS

Can you complete this mini crossword using the picture clues?

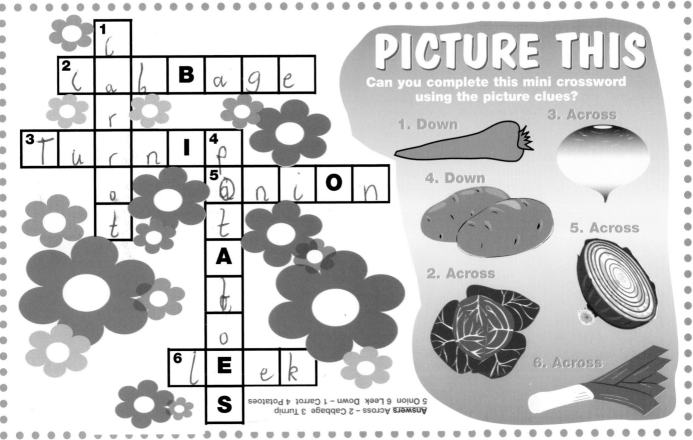

1. Down
3. Across
4. Down
5. Across
2. Across
6. Across

Across — 2 Cabbage 3 Turnip 5 Onion 6 Leek Down — 1 Carrot 4 Potatoes

15

Join Becky and Sophie Ashford at Tangletrees Pet Hotel – an amazing holiday centre for animals, large and small

PET HOTEL

Little Guest – BIG Problems!

1

OSCAR'S SUCH A SOFTIE WHEN YOU'RE HERE, MRS FITZ.

HE'S NORMALLY A REAL GROUCH.

HE JUST TAKES A WHILE TO GET TO KNOW PEOPLE.

2

YOU'VE CERTAINLY GOT A WAY WITH ANIMALS, ANGELA.

I DON'T HAVE ANY TRAINING, I'M AFRAID.

YOU'RE A NATURAL!

6

NOW SIDNEY'S A LITTLE BIT SHY.

I CAN'T WAIT TO SEE HIM.

WE'VE NEVER LOOKED AFTER A TARANTULA BEFORE.

7

A SPIDER! I DIDN'T REALISE... I THINK YOU HAD BETTER CHECK SIDNEY IN, DAN, I CAN HEAR THE DOGS BARKING UPSTAIRS.

8

WELL, MR DENHAM SHALL WE GO THROUGH SIDNEY'S CARE PLAN?

THAT'S FUNNY, I DIDN'T HEAR THE DOGS.

THAT'S STRANGE, WE LEFT BERTIE AND CHARLIE PLAYING IN THE MEADOW.

11

MRS FITZGERALD, WE WONDERED WHERE YOU HAD GOT TO.

HOW'S THE NEW ARRIVAL GETTING ON?

12

WOULD YOU LIKE TO HOLD HIM, MRS FITZ?

PERHAPS LATER, BECKS, I'M A BIT BUSY AT THE MO'!

COME AND HAVE A LOOK.

13

BUT JAKE'S TEACHING US ALL ABOUT SPIDERS!

ER, WELL YES, OF COURSE...

I CAN'T TEACH MRS FITZ ANYTHING, SOPHIE, I'M SURE SHE HAS HELD A SPIDER BEFORE.

Words: Mandy Archer ✿ Cartoonist: Paul Jones

Don't miss the *Girl Talk* Pet Hotel books,

available from all good retailers, priced £2.99 each

Every year, thousands of young people attend stage schools throughout the country with one thing in mind – making it big! However, from all those hopefuls only a handful will eventually become the famous faces of tomorrow. Girl Talk predicts these six young ladies will be among the lucky few and grabs a quick word with the rising stars of the next generation

Jade Turnbull

Jade is the TV actress best known for her performance as independent, tough-cookie Regina O'Hagan in CBBC's *Byker Grove*. Her megastar potential was recognised by TV documentary *The Fame Game*. The programme followed her progress from audition to the screen in *Byker*. Jade is looking forward to the year 2000 and she has two ambitions for the new millennium – to be a millionaire and a superstar!

FACT FILE
Age ten
Family two brothers, Aidan and Dean
Pets two fish, Betty and Birty
Favourite TV programmes *EastEnders* and *Friends*
Five words which best describe you happy, lovable, untidy, talkative and funny

Words: Nora Kearns

Stars NEW MI

Camilla Hunsley

When Camilla was only three years old she took her first ballet exam and did so well she was graded as a six-year-old. Her ballet teacher was so impressed she suggested to Camilla's parents that they enroll her in a stage school. Camilla's parents took the advice and soon after – at the age of four – Camilla landed her first acting job. She played the part of a young girl pretending to be an astronaut for the launch of Nickelodeon. Since then, Camilla has done lots of work on television. She loves acting and dancing and hopes to have a successful career doing both. Camilla has also appeared on the cover of *Girl Talk.*

FACT FILE
Age nine
Family only child
Pets two cats, Jazz and Gio
Favourite television programme *Smart Guy*
Five words which best describe you a cat-loving enthusiastic Sagittarius

Miranda has been lucky enough to work all over Europe and has featured in TV advertisements. Miranda's first modelling job was when she was two and a half – she appeared on a knitting pattern. Since then she has been in newspaper adverts, on magazine covers (including *Girl Talk!*) and acted in pantomime. Miranda goes to drama school once a week and her ambition for the next millennium is to be a good film actress.

FACT FILE
Age 12
Family one sister, Melanie
Pets a rabbit, Babes
Favourite TV programme *Sister Sister*
Five words which best describe you perfectionist, serious, ambitious, loyal and sociable

Home Farm Twins

Polly and Sophie Duniam are better known as Hannah and Helen Moore from the television series *Home Farm Twins*. The girls had been in a film called *Dance to the Music of Time* and had appeared in some TV advertisements, but they couldn't believe their luck when they were chosen from 56 sets of twins for the programme. Like the twins in the series, they moved from the city to the country and now live on a farm.

FACT FILE ON POLLY
Age 12
Family twin sister Sophie
Pets a pony called Dusty
Favourite television programme *Grange Hill*
Five words which best describe you sporty, animal-lover, untidy, loud and flirty

FACT FILE ON SOPHIE
Age 12 (one minute older than Polly)
Family twin sister Polly
Pets a pony called Dusty (they share him!)
Favourite television programme *The Wild House*
Five words which best describe you funny, sporty, happy, friendly, and loving

of the MILLENNIUM

Dominique Moore

After attending some regular drama classes, Dominique auditioned successfully for a part in the musical *Oliver!* Dominique was also an orphan in *Annie* (her progress was shown in the BBC programme *Paddington Green*) and in the chorus for *Whistle Down the Wind*. She has also appeared on CBBC's *Live & Kicking* and *Blue Peter*. Dominique is described by her agent as a "born entertainer – someone who can make everyone laugh".

Miranda Hutcheon

FACT FILE
Age 13
Family two sisters, Tania and Shamala
Pets two fish – with no names!
Favourite Television Programme *Moesha*
Five words which best describe you intelligent, lively, talkative, bubbly and very, very lucky!

Dominique Moore and Lia Saville, who appeared with her in *Paddington Green*

Bake-Tastic 2000!

Want to make your millennium celebration really special? Vicky, the Girl Talk cook, shows you how with some great recipes

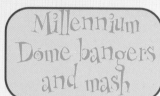

21st century chunky chocolate cookies

These double-chocolate cookies are perfect for sleepover midnight feasts. This recipe will make 18 cookies. If you don't want to make them all at once, keep your leftover raw cookie dough wrapped in plastic film in the fridge. But when you've tasted them, we're sure you'll want to cook them all at once!

WHAT YOU NEED

✿ 250g butter, softened
✿ 50g caster sugar
✿ 100g light brown sugar
✿ 300g self-raising flour
✿ 2 tbsp milk
✿ 100g plain chocolate, very roughly chopped
✿ 75g milk chocolate, very roughly chopped
✿ 50g walnuts, roughly chopped (optional)

WHAT TO DO

1 Preheat the oven to 180C/Gas 4. Line two or three baking sheets with baking parchment. In a bowl, beat together the butter and sugars until light and fluffy. Use an electric hand whisk for speed.
2 Stir in the flour and milk. Mix well then stir in the chocolate and the nuts.
3 Divide the mixture into 18 equal portions. Roughly shape each portion into a ball. Put on the baking sheets well spaced out to allow for spreading. (You may have to cook these in batches). Lightly flatten each biscuit with your fingertips, keeping the mixture quite rough looking.
4 Bake for 15–20 minutes until the cookies are a pale golden colour around the edges, but still feel soft in the centre. Cool on the baking sheet for 5 minutes then, using a palette knife, transfer to a wire rack and allow to cool a little more before eating. Makes 18.

Millennium Dome bangers and mash

If you're having a special New Year's Day lunch, why not celebrate the start of the new millennium with good old sausage and mash, specially shaped like the Millennium Dome?

WHAT YOU NEED

✿ 1 onion
✿ 1 tbsp vegetable oil
✿ 8 thin sausages, pork (chipolatas)
✿ 700g white potatoes
✿ 15g butter
✿ splash of milk
✿ 300ml chicken stock

WHAT TO DO

1 Cut the onion in half, remove and throw away the skin. Thinly slice the onion. Heat the oil in a saucepan and add the onion. Cook for 15 minutes over a low heat, stirring occasionally until golden brown.
2 Meanwhile, preheat the grill. Cook the sausages under the grill for about 25–30 minutes, turning occasionally until the sausages are cooked through.
3 While the sausages are cooking peel and cut the potatoes into chunks. Put into a large pan. Cover with cold water, then bring to the boil. Cover with a lid and cook for 15 minutes until the potatoes are tender.
4 Drain the potatoes, then return to the pan. Add the butter and milk and mash with a potato masher until the potatoes are completely mashed. Keep warm.
5 Add the stock to the onions, then bring to the boil over a medium heat. Boil for 5 minutes, stirring occasionally.
6 To serve, spoon the potatoes on to a large serving plate and, using the back of a spoon, smooth into a dome shape. Stick the sausages in, so they stick out like the masts of the real Millennium Dome. Pour over the hot onion gravy. Serve straight away. Serves four.

Y2K brownies

Everyone loves gooey chocolate brownies. Make your Y2K (or year 2000) brownies more special by adding even more chocolate. We've drizzled white and dark chocolate over the top. The secret is to drizzle with quick movements for a really professional effect.

WHAT YOU NEED

✿ 100g plain chocolate
✿ 75g butter
✿ 225g golden caster sugar
✿ 2 eggs
✿ 1 tsp vanilla extract
✿ 75g plain flour

✿ Recipes: Vicky Musselman ✿ Illustrations: Rachel Fuller

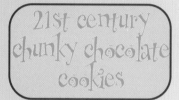

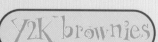

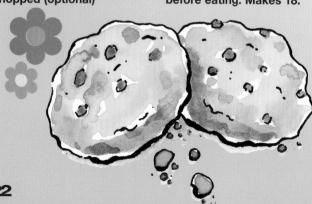

- ½ tsp baking powder
- ½ tsp salt
- 50g walnuts, chopped
- 50g white chocolate

WHAT TO DO

1 Grease and line the bottom of a 20cm square tin. (If you don't have square, a round one is fine.)
2 Break up half the plain chocolate and put in a heatproof bowl with the butter and sugar. Place the bowl over a pan of simmering water and allow the chocolate to melt.
3 Allow to cool for 5 minutes, then stir in the eggs, vanilla extract, flour, baking powder, salt and walnuts. Stir well until the mixture is smooth.
4 Pour into the prepared tin. Bake for 35 minutes until firm around the edges. Allow to cool in the tin.
5 Melt the remaining plain chocolate and white chocolate in separate bowls. Using a teaspoon, drizzle over half the white chocolate in a squiggly pattern all over the top. Follow this with a drizzle of dark chocolate, then finish with a layer of white. Cut into squares. Makes 16.

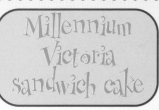

Millennium Victoria sandwich cake

This traditional sponge is sandwiched together with a creamy icing and your favourite jam. To make the cake special, we've decorated the top with the number 2000. It makes a great centrepiece to a New Year's Day party.

WHAT YOU NEED

- 175g butter, softened
- 175g sugar
- 3 eggs
- 175g self-raising flour
- your favourite jam, for spreading
- 200g packet soft cheese, like Philadelphia
- 100g icing sugar, plus extra for dusting

WHAT TO DO

1 Preheat the oven to 190C/Gas 5. Grease two 18cm sandwich tins then line the base of each with a circle of greaseproof paper. Tip the butter and sugar into a bowl. Beat well with a wooden spoon until the mixture is pale and fluffy. This will take at least 5 minutes.
2 Crack the eggs into a bowl, and lightly beat with a fork. Slowly add the eggs to the sugar and butter mixture a little at a time, beating well after each addition.
3 Sift over the flour. Using a large metal spoon, gently fold the flour into the creamed mixture. Take care not to overmix or you will knock out the air you've already beaten in.
4 Divide the mixture between the two tins and carefully smooth the top with the back of a spoon. Bake for 25–30 minutes until risen and golden, and when a skewer is inserted it comes out clean.
5 Allow the cakes to cool for a few minutes before turning them out on to a wire rack. Peel off the paper and leave to cool completely.
6 While the cakes are cooling make the icing. Whisk the soft cheese with an electric hand whisk to soften it. (If you don't have an electric hand whisk, use a wooden spoon). Add the icing sugar a little at a time, whisking to a smooth icing.
7 When the cake is cold, spread jam on one half of the cake and the icing over the other. Sandwich together. Cut out a figure two (2) and three zeros (0) from a sheet of greaseproof and place on top of the cake to spell out 2000. Dust with a thick layer of icing sugar, then carefully peel away the greaseproof paper to reveal the design. Cuts into eight.

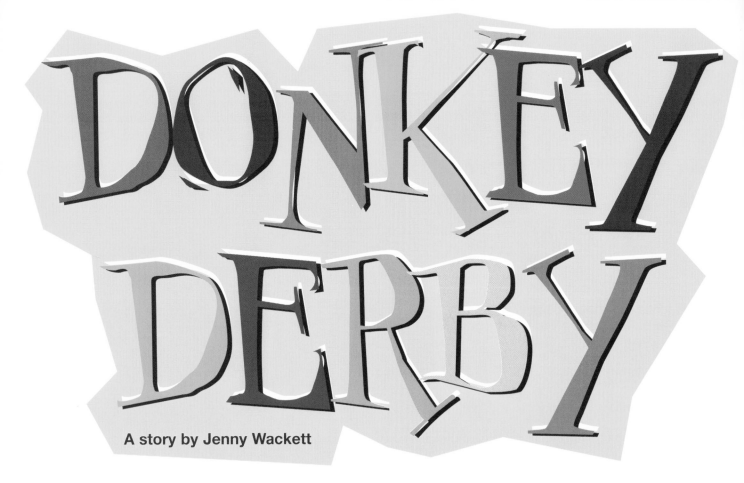

DONKEY DERBY

A story by Jenny Wackett

Illustration: Carol Daniel

> Joely was determined to find a way to save Sparky and his friends at the donkey sanctuary

Joely Peterson loved animals. She owned two cats called Po and Tato, a big hairy dog called Bumble, and Arthur, a cheeky, blue and white budgie. Even though she loved her pets, her favourite thing was working at the donkey sanctuary at the weekends.

"I don't know how you fit it all in!" said Jamilla, helping her best friend fill Arthur's food tray with fresh seed.

Joely laughed. "If it wasn't for me and Mrs Townsend, they'd have no one to look after them, and what would happen to Sparky then?"

Sparky was Joely's favourite donkey. He was grey all over apart from his two front feet, which were white.

On Saturday morning Joely's dad drove her to the sanctuary. All the donkeys were grazing in the fields. As soon as Sparky spotted Joely he trotted over to greet her.

"Hello, Sparky!" she said. "I think I know what you're after!" She gave Sparky a couple of sugar cubes from her pocket and rubbed him affectionately on the nose.

Joely spent the morning mucking out the stables and replacing the old bedding with clean, golden straw. By the time she got round to refilling the donkeys' troughs with fresh food, it was time to go home. As Joely walked through the yard, she could see her dad with Mrs Townsend.

School sponsors

"I don't know what I'm going to do," Joely heard Mrs Townsend say. "There's a huge hole in the stable roof and there isn't enough money to pay for it. Our funds are so low it's getting harder and harder to keep this place open."

"You're not closing the sanctuary, are you?" asked Joely.

"We might have to if we don't make some money, soon." replied Mrs Townsend.

"What am I going to do, Milly?" Joely asked Jamilla at school on Monday.

"I don't know – couldn't you have a raffle or a sponsored swim?"

"How about getting our school to sponsor a donkey?" said Joely.

"But, that's only one donkey," pointed out Jamilla.

"Then we'll ask the other schools in the county to sponsor a donkey, too." Joely was so excited by her idea that she went straight to her headmistress's office.

"That's a very interesting idea." said Mrs Winters, the headmistress. "I think we should propose it to the other schools."

By the end of the week, all the other schools in the area had sponsored a donkey. Best of all, Joely's school had sponsored Sparky.

"With the schools' sponsorship we'll be able to care for the donkeys all year round," said Mrs Townsend to Joely the following weekend. "But we still need to find the money to repair the stable roof," she sighed.

Starters orders

That evening, Joely was eating her tea and trying to think of money-making ideas. While munching on a mouthful of sweet corn Joely had a brain wave.

"A donkey derby!" she shouted, making her mum jump. "Each school could enter their donkey and we could have an afternoon of races. We

could even charge a small entrance fee for visitors!"

"That's a great idea, love, but what will the winners receive?"

"The winning donkey could have a lovely rosette and the winning school could be given a winner's certificate." After explaining her idea to Mrs Townsend, the pair of them set to work making preparations.

When the day of the Donkey Derby finally arrived the sanctuary was full of people.

Joely led Sparky to the starting line with the other donkeys who were in his heat and waited for the first race to begin.

"Just do your best," said Joely, giving him a rub behind his long grey ears.

Sparky did just that! To Joely's delighted amazement, Sparky won his heat *and* the donkey derby finals. "Thanks to your help and generosity, we can now repair the stable roofs," Mrs Townsend announced to everyone present after awarding Joely and Sparky the winner's rosette and certificate. "And because you have all made today's event such a success, we will be holding another one next year!"

Derby star

The next day, Joely was back at the sanctuary making sure that all of the donkeys got their carrots and apples, as well as giving Sparky a couple of sugar lumps as a treat for winning. "You were the star of the derby," Joely told him.

"Hee-haw," replied Sparky.

"Hello, Joely," Mrs Townsend called to Joely from her office. "I've got something for you."

"What is it?" Joely asked when Mrs Townsend handed her a parcel.

"It's to say thank you for all your hard work," Mrs Townsend replied. "Go on, open it."

Joely carefully unwrapped the parcel. Inside was the front page of the local newspaper, mounted in a picture frame. Printed above a picture of Joely and Sparky was the headline, "The donkey sanctuary's bright spark!"

"It's about me!" exclaimed Joely in surprise.

"Of course," said Mrs Townsend. "After all, the derby was your sparky idea in the first place!" ✿

WHICH IS THE CAREER FOR YOU?

What career do you see yourself following in the new millennium? Try our quiz to find the job that suits you best

1 You're running out of money and are bored with your old clothes. How do you jazz up your wardrobe?

a) You visit your local charity shop to hunt for some bargains and – most importantly – you know your money will be going towards a good cause.

b) You buy new buttons and some fake fur trim to sew on to your old tops to give them a brand new look.

c) You arrange to get together with your friends and swap – that way their old clothes will be new to you and yours will be new to them!

2 You had a big argument with your best friend at school and now you feel very upset. What do you do?

a) Ring your friend as soon as you get home from school to try to make up, even if you think the row wasn't all your fault.

b) Decide to write down how the row has made you feel and put it in a letter to your friend.

c) Think carefully about why you argued then talk to your friend about it so that you make sure you don't fall out over it ever again.

3 For homework you have been asked to do a project on any topic you like. Which would you choose?

a) You write a story about all your pets because you really enjoy looking after them and love talking about them more than anything else.

b) You sketch out some fashion designs and include lots of samples of different fabrics to show how the clothes would look

Words: Kelly Wilks ✩ Illustrations: Katy Taggart

when they are made up.

c) You write an essay on famous inventions, which means doing some cool research into their inventors.

4 **Your mum doesn't feel at all well and has been told to stay in bed for the weekend. What do you do?**

a) You go and check on her every hour, you take her drinks and snacks and make sure she has everything she needs.

b) You try cheering her up by painting a really colourful picture to brighten up her room and you read her a story which you have written all by yourself.

c) You organise all the chores between you and your brothers or sisters, so your mum doesn't have to worry about the housework piling up.

5 **What type of television programmes do you most enjoy watching?**

a) You never miss an episode of *Animal Hospital* and you get really upset when you see the injured animals at the beginning of the show.

b) You love *SMart* and *Changing Rooms* as they give you great ideas for things you can make yourself.

c) You love watching thrillers like *See How They Run* and trying to work out what will happen at the end. It's great when you find that you have guessed correctly!

6 **Your birthday is coming up soon and your parents want to know what you would like. What do you ask for?**

a) You would like a bigger hutch for your rabbits and guinea pigs, so that there is more room for them to move around – or for even more pets!

b) You would love an artist's palette and easel so you can work on your masterpieces just like the professionals do.

c) You want a science set packed with test tubes and chemicals so you can carry out your own experiments.

7 **Your school is putting on its annual play and they need people to help out. How do you offer to help?**

a) You agree to help the cast with their costume changes and prepare sandwiches and drinks for them during the interval.

b) You offer to help design and paint the scenery, and even offer to make some of the costumes and props.

c) You volunteer to take

charge of selling the tickets so that they can be sure of having a full audience to perform to.

8 **Your dad tells you he has been promoted at work, but it means moving to another part of the country. What's the first thing you think about?**

a) How much you'll miss all your friends and relations if you have to move away from them all.

b) You're already planning how to decorate your new bedroom!

c) Although you're sorry to leave, you're excited by the idea of exploring a new area and researching your new home town.

★ HOW DID YOU SCORE? ★

Mostly A's
You're a real softy, aren't you? In fact, you're so caring you're destined for the sort of job which will allow you to be caring all day, and get paid for it! Think about training to be a nurse, social worker or vet – if you haven't thought about it already, that is. Meantime, why not consider helping a local charity in your spare time? They may welcome help from volunteers.

Mostly B's
You've got a very strong creative streak and it would be wasted if you didn't consider an artistic career. Think about being an author or journalist, interior designer, architect or even a designer on your favourite magazine, *Girl Talk!*

Mostly C's
You have a very level-headed attitude towards life, which means you are good at making clear and sure decisions. Why don't you consider a job in business or a scientific career? Professions that might suit you would include doctor, accountant or lawyer. However you decide, you can count on making lots of money!

PUZZLES

Try these teasers at your leisure!

BOOKWORM

Here are four descriptions of famous books, but they each have one deliberate mistake. Can you spot them?

1 *The Sheep Pig* was written by Dirk *Dick* King-Smith.

2 *Peter Pan* is the story of a little girl *boy* who never grew up.

3 The story of Hansel and Gretta *Gretal* is a classic fairy tale.

4 Hans Christian Andersen wrote about an ugly duckling which grew into a beautiful peacock. *Swan*

Answers: 1 The author's name is Dick King-Smith. 2 Peter Pan is a little boy. 3 Hansel and Gretel. 4 The Ugly Duckling grew up to be a swan.

Stargazing

Can you work out which famous people are browsing through *Girl Talk*?

Answers 1 Billie 2 Toby Anstis 3 Bart Simpson 4 Barbara Windsor – Peggy Mitchell from *EastEnders*

Go fly a kite

Tia, Lauren and Jade are playing together in the park, but can you tell which one is flying the kite?

Answer Tia

A QUESTION OF SPORT

Cross out all the letters that appear in the grid more than once to reveal a hidden sport

A	F	N	H	D	G	J	B
I	Q	P	S	U	O	R	P
L	B	C	M	A	I	F	S
D	R	G	U	V	K	Q	V
F	E	T	P	N	V	R	L
J	M	A	T	Y	I	G	B

Answer Hockey

TRICKY TRAINERS

There are five differences between these two pairs of trainers. Can you find them all?

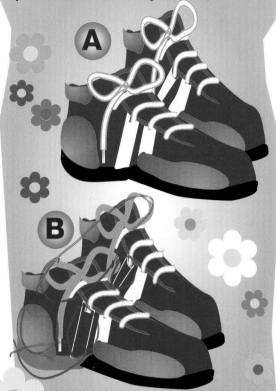

A

B

Answers Trainers B are different shades of blue and red, they have only one white stripe, they have grey laces and the heel is a different colour.

LEISURE CENTRE

Can you find all these hobbies and pastimes hidden in the word square?

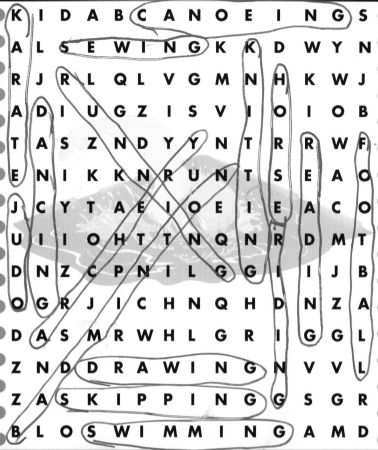

K	I	D	A	B	C	A	N	O	E	I	N	G	S
A	L	S	E	W	I	N	G	K	K	D	W	Y	N
R	J	R	L	Q	L	V	G	M	N	H	K	W	J
A	D	I	U	G	Z	I	S	V	I	O	I	O	B
T	A	S	Z	N	D	Y	Y	N	T	R	R	W	F
E	N	I	K	K	N	R	U	N	T	S	E	A	O
J	C	Y	T	A	E	I	O	E	I	E	A	C	O
U	I	I	O	H	T	T	N	Q	N	R	D	M	T
D	N	Z	C	P	N	I	L	G	G	I	I	J	B
O	G	R	J	I	C	H	N	Q	H	D	N	Z	A
D	A	S	M	R	W	H	L	G	R	I	G	G	L
Z	N	D	D	R	A	W	I	N	G	N	V	V	L
Z	A	S	K	I	P	P	I	N	G	G	S	G	R
B	L	O	S	W	I	M	M	I	N	G	A	M	D

READING DANCING HORSE RIDING
CANOEING KARATE ARCHERY JUDO
BADMINTON SWIMMING RUNNING
DRAWING SKIPPING KNITTING SEWING
SKATING FOOTBALL

Book ends

Rearrange these mixed-up book titles and see if you can spot the odd one out

1 BACLKUBATYE

2 HETOINLGKNI

3 EBAB

4 UTSREEARSNDILA

Answers 1 Black Beauty 2 The Lion King 3 Babe 4 Treasure Island Number 4 is the odd one out as it is not about animals.

A STITCH IN TIME

See if you can work out a popular hobby by rearranging the first letter of the names of these objects

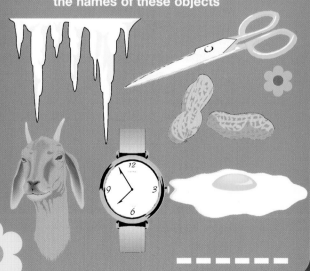

Girl TALK 2000 YEAR

NOTES

	JANUARY	FEBRUARY	MARCH	APRIL	MAY	JUNE
1	SAT ✿ New Year's Day	TUE	WED	SAT	MON ✿ May Bank Holiday	THU
2	SUN	WED	THU	SUN ✿ Mother's Day	TUE ✿ Back to school!	FRI
3	MON ✿ New Year's Holiday	THU	FRI	MON	WED	SAT
4	TUE	FRI	SAT	TUE	THU	SUN
5	WED	SAT ✿ Yuan Tan (Chinese New Year)	SUN	WED ✿ Al-Hijra (Muslim New Year's Day)	FRI	MON ✿ World Environment Day
6	THU	SUN	MON	THU	SAT	TUE
7	FRI	MON	TUE	FRI	SUN	WED
8	SAT	TUE	WED	SAT	MON	THU
9	SUN	WED	THU	SUN	TUE	FRI
10	MON	THU	FRI	MON	WED	SAT
11	TUE	FRI	SAT	TUE	THU	SUN
12	WED	SAT	SUN	WED	FRI	MON
13	THU	SUN	MON ✿ Commonwealth Day	THU	SAT	TUE
14	FRI	MON ✿ Valentine's Day	TUE	FRI ✿ Break up for Easter	SUN	WED
15	SAT	TUE	WED	SAT	MON	THU
16	SUN	WED	THU	SUN	TUE	FRI
17	MON	THU	FRI	MON	WED	SAT
18	TUE	FRI	SAT	TUE	THU	SUN ✿ Father's Day
19	WED	SAT	SUN	WED	FRI	MON
20	THU	SUN	MON	THU	SAT	TUE
21	FRI	MON ✿ Half-term break	TUE	FRI ✿ Good Friday ✿ The Queen's real birthday (Her official one moves around!)	SUN	WED
22	SAT	TUE ✿ Girl Talk's 5th birthday!	WED	SAT	MON	THU
23	SUN	WED	THU	SUN ✿ Easter Sunday	TUE	FRI
24	MON	THU	FRI	MON	WED	SAT
25	TUE	FRI	SAT	TUE	THU	SUN
26	WED	SAT	SUN ✿ British Summer Time begins (Clocks go forward one hour)	WED	FRI	MON
27	THU	SUN	MON	THU	SAT	TUE
28	FRI	MON	TUE	FRI	SUN	WED
29	SAT	TUE	WED	SAT	MON ✿ Spring Bank Holiday ✿ Half-term again!	THU
30	SUN		THU	SUN	TUE	FRI ✿ Summer holidays time (If you live in Scotland)
31	MON		FRI		WED	

PS Make sure you get your copy of Girl Talk every other Wednesday

PLANNER

JULY	AUGUST	SEPTEMBER	OCTOBER	NOVEMBER	DECEMBER	
SAT	TUE	FRI	SUN	WED	FRI	1
SUN	WED	SAT	MON	THU	SAT	2
MON	THU	SUN	TUE	FRI	SUN	3
TUE	FRI	MON	WED	SAT	MON	4
WED	SAT	TUE	THU	SUN ✿ Guy Fawkes (Bonfire) Night	TUE	5
THU	SUN	WED	FRI	MON	WED	6
FRI	MON	THU	SAT	TUE	THU	7
SAT	TUE	FRI	SUN	WED	FRI	8
SUN	WED	SAT	MON ✿ Yom Kippur (Day when Jews ask for God's forgiveness)	THU	SAT	9
MON	THU	SUN	TUE	FRI	SUN	10
TUE	FRI	MON	WED	SAT	MON	11
WED	SAT	TUE	THU	SUN	TUE	12
THU	SUN	WED	FRI	MON	WED	13
FRI	MON	THU	SAT	TUE	THU	14
SAT	TUE	FRI	SUN	WED	FRI	15
SUN	WED	SAT	MON	THU	SAT	16
MON	THU	SUN	TUE	FRI	SUN	17
TUE	FRI	MON	WED	SAT	MON	18
WED	SAT	TUE	THU	SUN	TUE	19
THU	SUN	WED	FRI	MON	WED	20
FRI ✿ Summer holidays time (Throughout the UK except for Scotland)	MON	THU	SAT	TUE	THU	21
SAT	TUE	FRI	SUN	WED	FRI ✿ Hanukah begins	22
SUN	WED ✿ Janmashtami (the birthday of Lord Krishna)	SAT	MON	THU	SAT	23
MON	THU	SUN	TUE	FRI	SUN ✿ Ramadan ends	24
TUE	FRI	MON	WED	SAT	MON ✿ Christmas Day (Christian festival celebrating the birth of Jesus)	25
WED	SAT	TUE	THU	SUN ✿ Ramadan begins (Muslim festival of fasting from dawn to dusk)	TUE	26
THU	SUN	WED	FRI ✿ Diwali begins (Hindu New Year and Hindu and Sikh Festival of Lights)	MON	WED	27
FRI	MON ✿ Summer Bank Holiday	THU	SAT	TUE	THU	28
SAT	TUE	FRI	SUN ✿ British Summer Time ends (Put those clocks back one hour!)	WED	FRI	29
SUN	WED	SAT ✿ Rosh Hashana (Jewish New Year)	MON	THU	SAT	30
MON	THU		TUE ✿ Halloween		SUN	31

NOTES

NB Some major religious festivals are not fixed dates and should be confirmed nearer the time. Also, the school-term dates given are for the majority of schools, but these vary across the country and should be checked

Drawing is loads of fun. It's something you can do anytime – wherever you are. With just a little practice you can draw all sorts of things. So let's get arty!

TOP MARKS!

FUN FACES

YOU WILL NEED
✿ Drawing paper ✿ Pencil ✿ Rubber

DRAWING A FACE

1 First draw an oval shape with a centre guideline (A). Next draw in lines for eyes (B), the mouth (C), and for the end of nose (D). Then draw in two vertical lines (E). The points where line 2 crosses line 5 mark the centre of the eyes.
2 Draw in eyes, nose and mouth, like this.
3 Then add ears, using a simple oval shape cut in half.
4 Draw in your favourite hairstyle to complete the face.
5 Do lots of practice faces using the guide lines. When you feel confident, try drawing some face shapes without the guide lines. Then practise judging the right positions for the features by sight and have a go at drawing some more fun faces!

FIGURE DRAWING

FASHION SHOW

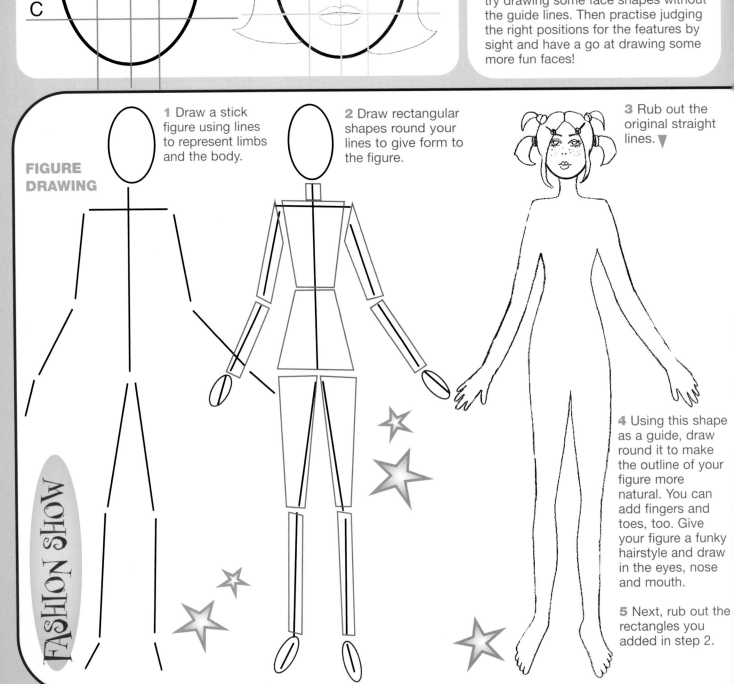

1 Draw a stick figure using lines to represent limbs and the body.

2 Draw rectangular shapes round your lines to give form to the figure.

3 Rub out the original straight lines. ▼

4 Using this shape as a guide, draw round it to make the outline of your figure more natural. You can add fingers and toes, too. Give your figure a funky hairstyle and draw in the eyes, nose and mouth.

5 Next, rub out the rectangles you added in step 2.

PRETTY AS A PICTURE

PET PORTRAIT

Drawing from a photograph is a good way to improve your artistic skills. When you've finished find a fun frame for it and hang your art up on the wall. Then, if you draw lots of pictures, you can have your own gallery in your bedroom!

1

Get a good photo of your pet – use a colour photocopy if you don't want to spoil your snap.

2

Divide it into a grid of eight squares.

YOU WILL NEED
✿ Photograph of your pet or favourite animal ✿ Drawing paper ✿ Pencil ✿ Rubber

3

Now draw a rectangle the same size as your pic on a piece of drawing paper and divide it up the same way.

6 All you need to add now is a fab fashion outfit and your drawing is complete.

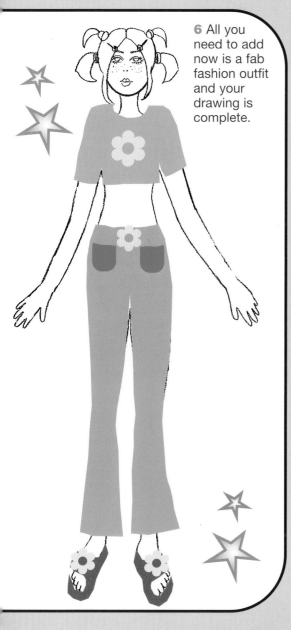

Copy the contents of each square from the photo into the matching squares on the drawing paper. Then rub out your grid lines

4

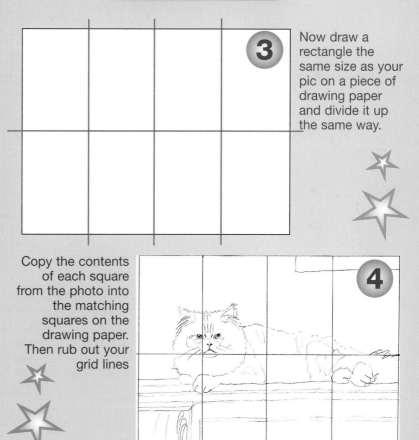

5

Now you can colour in your drawing. Use colouring pencils, paint or even have a go using pastels.

✿ Words and pictures: Carol Gook

Junk mirror frame

This funky frame will be the showpiece of any bedroom wall – it's wild, wacky and totally original! Mark from SMart shows you how to make one for your room

Girl TALK Make

WHAT YOU'LL NEED

✿ **Thick card** ✿ **Mirror or mirror tile**
✿ **Assorted junk** ✿ **PVA glue** ✿ **Spray paint or paint** ✿ **Paintbrush** ✿ **Scissors**
✿ **Double-sided tape** ✿ **Paper** ✿ **Ruler**

Measure and cut out a thick piece of card which is 5cm bigger than your mirror all round.

1

2 **Stick your mirror firmly to the centre of the card.** Strong double-sided sticky tape works well.

3 Now cover the card edges with lots of PVA glue.

4 **This is where the fun begins!** Start sticking your junk on to the frame. You can use anything – badges, bows, bottle tops, whatever you can find. Make sure that it's packed with lots of different things. Now leave it to dry.

✿ Pictures: John Green ✿ Make-it: Lizi Botham

34

it!

5

Cover your mirror with a sheet of paper. This is so that you won't get paint on the glass. Make sure that it goes right up to the edges.

7

Remove the paper when you're sure the paint is dry.

Now you can paint it. Use a bright colour or gold or silver, which always look classy. You can use either spray paint or brush-on paint.

6

8

Hang it on your wall – and now you can admire your mirror frame as much as you admire yourself in it!

1

1477

Girls in 1477 wore clothes which really restricted their movements. In this painting mother and daughter are wearing nearly identical velvet dresses. The girl is wearing her hair in a type of hair band called a frontlet, which is also made of velvet. A child's hair could be worn out in a frontlet like this until she was about 14. But then it had to be covered up, like her mother's is in the tall cone on the back of her head! Would your mum go out shopping dressed like that? No, but neither did this lady, as she was obviously an aristocrat.

Lady Donne and her daughter

2

The family of Sir Robert Viner

The young girl in this painting is wearing a typical number from 1673. You had to be rich to have an outfit like this. The gown has a scooped neckline (handy for showing off your fancy jewellery!), fitted bodice, elbow-length sleeves with embroidered cuffs, an overskirt looped up at the back and a lace-trimmed underskirt. This girl probably had a private tutor, but imagine getting ready for school in the mornings if you had to wear all that!

1673

FASHION THROUGH

Are you a dedicated follower of fashion? If so, you'll be interested in having a peek at what young girls have worn over the last millennium

5

Brown wool dress

1880

During winter in the late 1800s this kind of woollen outfit was worn with button-up boots. It must have itched like mad and it would have taken ages to do up all the buttons. Thank heavens for today's puffa jackets!

If you think *your* school uniform is dull, take a look at this early example of the famous gymslip and blouse. This one is from 1939. By that time, dresses had become shorter and running for the bus wasn't a problem, but the girls and boys would still have had to go into school by separate entrances.

1939

6

School uniform

1800

Can't you just see yourself, in 1800, skipping along to your best friend's birthday party wearing this dress? With your hair in ringlets (which would have meant sleeping with your hair rolled up in rags all night!) and flat pumps, this is not the kind of outfit you could wear while playing a game of rounders.

White organza and silk dress

Printed cotton girls dress

1830

If you lived in the 1830s, you would wear this dress with flat pumps, short gloves and a straw bonnet that tied in a big bow under your chin. Remember that in these and earlier times, children were expected to be seen and not heard. There was no girl power in 1830!

THE MILLENNIUM

White smocked dress

Patchwork dress

1930·45·60

During the war years material was in short supply and even in 1945, when this patchwork dress was made, there was a shortage of cloth. As goods were rationed, fabric had to be made by special, government-approved methods and labelled with a symbol, the 'utility' mark. This showed the cloth had been made in a careful, economical way. This dress would probably have been made from leftover fabric scraps.

- The smocked dress was typical of those worn by very young girls in the 1930s, '40s and '50s. There were no fashion garments for little sisters in those times, unlike now! Why not ask if you can look through the family album for pictures of your female relatives wearing something like this when they were three or four?

Modern fashion

Now, this looks more familiar! At the end of the 20th century, fashion for girls is fun, stylish and, above all, comfortable. But what will *your* grandchildren make of this kind of outfit? Maybe they'll laugh at old pictures of you and wonder how on earth you could walk around "looking like that"!

1999

✿ Words: Nora Kearns ✿ Picture 2 courtesy of the National Portrait Gallery, London. Thanks to Kate Bines at Bethnal Green Museum of Childhood, (0181) 983 5200, which houses the largest collection of children's costume in the country

Storm

a story by Katie Bright

Spending half-term with Dad was a treat, but the break held some stranger surprises in store for Naomi

Naomi had never seen such a battered old caravan. "It must be a hundred years old," she said to Dad.

Dad laughed. "Your gran loved this caravan. When we were kids we came here every holiday. Come on, let's get inside before we drown."

It was pouring with rain but Naomi didn't care. She didn't get to see her dad very often. Now she was going to spend all half-term with him, and in a caravan! That had been a fantastic surprise. It was cosy inside the caravan. Naomi loved her tiny bedroom.

"When it's clear you can see the sea from your window," said Dad. While Naomi unpacked she listened to the rain drumming on the roof. It didn't sound like it would ever stop. But Dad had said Gran's caravan was on a proper site with a café and a shop. And it wasn't far to the town, so there would be lots to do, even if it was wet and cold.

"Let's go down to the café," said Dad when they had finished making up Naomi's bed.

Under alien attack

On the way they met Sue and her daughter, Louise, from the caravan next door. Louise grinned at Naomi from under her big rain hat. "Great," she said, "someone my own age.

They've got some cool video games in the café. Want me to show you?" While Dad and Sue had a coffee and chatted, Naomi and Louise wandered over to the games with their colas.

"This is my favourite," said Louise. "Alien Attack. Have a go."

Naomi sat in the special chair and watched the screen. It was like flying through space in your own spaceship. "This is terrific," she said.

Louise nodded. "You know, I've seen a spaceship."

Naomi laughed.

"No, really," said Louise. "Last night, soon after we arrived, I looked out of my bedroom window and I saw all these lights floating over the sea."

Naomi began to feel a bit scared. "Maybe it was a plane," she said, "or a ship."

But Louise shook her head. "It wasn't. There were too many lights. It was weird."

When they were back in their caravan Naomi told Dad what Louise had said. Dad laughed. "Lights in the sky? They could be anything. Anyway, I don't know how Louise could see anything in this weather." Dad was right, of course, but Naomi couldn't help worrying. She couldn't get to sleep for a long time. What if it *was* an alien ship? What if the aliens wanted to attack Earth?

Run for it

But she must have fallen asleep eventually because suddenly she was wide awake. Water was dripping onto her face and the caravan was rocking from side to side. Were the aliens attacking? "Dad," she yelled. Dad came rushing in. "Water's coming in everywhere." He had to shout because the wind was howling and banging against the side of the caravan. "Grab some stuff. We'll have to go over to Sue's caravan."

Naomi pulled on her jeans and a jumper and pushed her feet into her boots. Her heart was pounding hard. It was difficult to stand up because the caravan was rocking around so much.

Naomi was nearly blown away when they opened the caravan door. Dad held on to her arm tightly. "Let's run for it," he shouted.

It wasn't far to Sue's caravan, but the wind was so strong and the ground so wet and slippery that it seemed to take forever to get there.

Lights at night

"Keep going," yelled Dad. But suddenly Naomi couldn't move. There, hovering over the sea, much too high in the sky to be a ship, were the strange lights. There were loads of them. Too many for an aeroplane. Louise was right, it was weird. It must be a spaceship. "Dad," she started to shout. But then, just as quickly as they had appeared, the lights vanished behind a cloud.

Once they were inside the caravan Sue fussed about them with towels and hot drinks and then started making up a bed for Dad on the living-room sofa.

"You'll have to share with Louise," she told Naomi. "It will be a squash, but at least it's dry!"

"Great," said Louise, "a sleepover!"

Once the girls were in Louise's bedroom, Naomi immediately told her what she had seen.

"Told you so," grinned Louise. "Let's keep watch. See if we can see the spaceship properly."

"Don't you think it's a bit scary?" asked Naomi.

Louise looked surprised. "No, I think it's exciting. Perhaps we'll get to visit other planets, like they do in *Star Trek Voyager.*"

"Maybe," said Naomi doubtfully. The girls knelt on the bed, their

Illustration: Rachel Fuller

Lights

noses pressed against the window, but they couldn't see anything.

What a night

Suddenly there was a terrible creaking and a huge crashing noise. Naomi and Louise stared at each other. Even Louise looked scared.
"Our caravan!" Dad was yelling.
The girls rushed out into the living room. Dad and Sue were standing by the open door staring at Gran's caravan. Naomi could hardly believe her eyes. It was lying completely on

its side, blown over by the wind.
"What a night," groaned Dad.
"I'm just glad we weren't in it," whispered Naomi. "First spaceships, now this."
By next morning the storm had blown away. It was bright and sunny when Naomi and Louise went outside to look around.
Dad was looking at Gran's overturned caravan. "Sue says we can stay with her until we fix this," he told Naomi.
But Naomi wasn't listening. She was staring. In the distance, rising out of

the sea, was a tall building on big metal legs.
"There's your spaceship, Louise," laughed Dad. "It's an oil rig. Wasn't there when I was a boy. They do look very strange lit up at night."
Louise looked disappointed, but Naomi was relieved. Their narrow escape from the caravan was quite enough adventure for one holiday.
"Never mind," she said to her new friend. "If we can't fly in a real spaceship, we might as well have a go in a pretend one. Want a game of Alien Attack?" ✿

available from all good retailers, priced £2.99 each

PUZZLES

Pit your wits against this jumble of puzzles

OUTER SPACE

Can you unscramble the names of these heavenly bodies then tell us which is the odd one out and why?

1 **SM RA**

2 **NSU**

3 **URS NAT**

4 **EV SNU**

Answers 1 Mars 2 Sun 3 Saturn 4 Venus
The sun is the odd one out because it is a star and not a planet.

PERFECT PROFESSIONS

Can you match these people to the jobs they are famous for doing?

a Artist
b Nurse
c Architect
d Cook
e Actor

1 Sir Christopher Wren
2 Delia Smith
3 Florence Nightingale
4 Terrence Hardiman
5 Vincent Van Gogh

Answers 1c 2d 3b 4e 5a

P... P... PICK UP A PENGUIN

How many penguins can you spot in this picture?

Answer There are 45 penguins.

THE KNOWLEDGE

Can you answer these general knowledge questions?

Across
1 If you really want something, you may have to beg or p l e a d (5) ✓
3 Mixing red and white will produce this colour (4) ✓
5 Some houses have one of these as an entrance (5) ✓
7 Another word meaning midday (4) ✓
8 A place where lots of apple trees grow (7) ✓
10 You learn to meditate doing this relaxing activity (4)
11 Use this to sweep the floor (5) ✓
13 We learn this from A to Z (8) ✓
14 You sometimes find this sticky stuff on the bark of trees (3) ✓

Down
1 People wear this red flower on their jackets on Remembrance Sunday (5) ✓
2 You hear with these parts of your body (4) ✓
3 The Pink P a n t h e r (7) ✓
4 England, Wales N Ireland and Scotland together make up the United k i n g d o m (7)
6 A unicorn has one on its forehead (4) ✓
9 Plant seeds in this to make the flowers grow (4) ✓
11 The name of a famous sheep-pig (4) ✓
12 Horses like to eat lots of these (4) ✓

Answers Across – 1 Plead 3 Pink 5 Porch 7 Noon 8 Orchard 10 Yoga 11 Broom 13 Alphabet 14 Sap Down – 1 Poppy 2 Ears 3 Panther 4 Kingdom 6 Horn 9 Soil 11 Babe 12 Oats

46

MAKE MORE WORDS

How many words of three letters or more can you make from this word?

INVENTIONS

We made an astounding 80 words! Can you beat that?

TELLY ADDICTS

Can you use the *Girl Talk* code to reveal the name of this TV programme?

A B C D E F G H I J K L M

N O P Q R S T U V W X Y Z

Answer The Home Farm Twins

PUZZLED POSTIE

The postman has mail for someone, but to which house will the letters be delivered?

B

A

C

D

WHAT'S MY NAME?

R A L P H

Answer Ralph

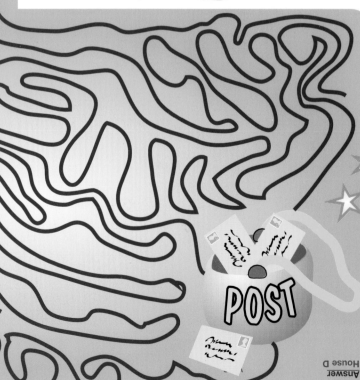

Can you reveal the name of this bunny by using the first letter from the names of these things?

POST

Answer House D

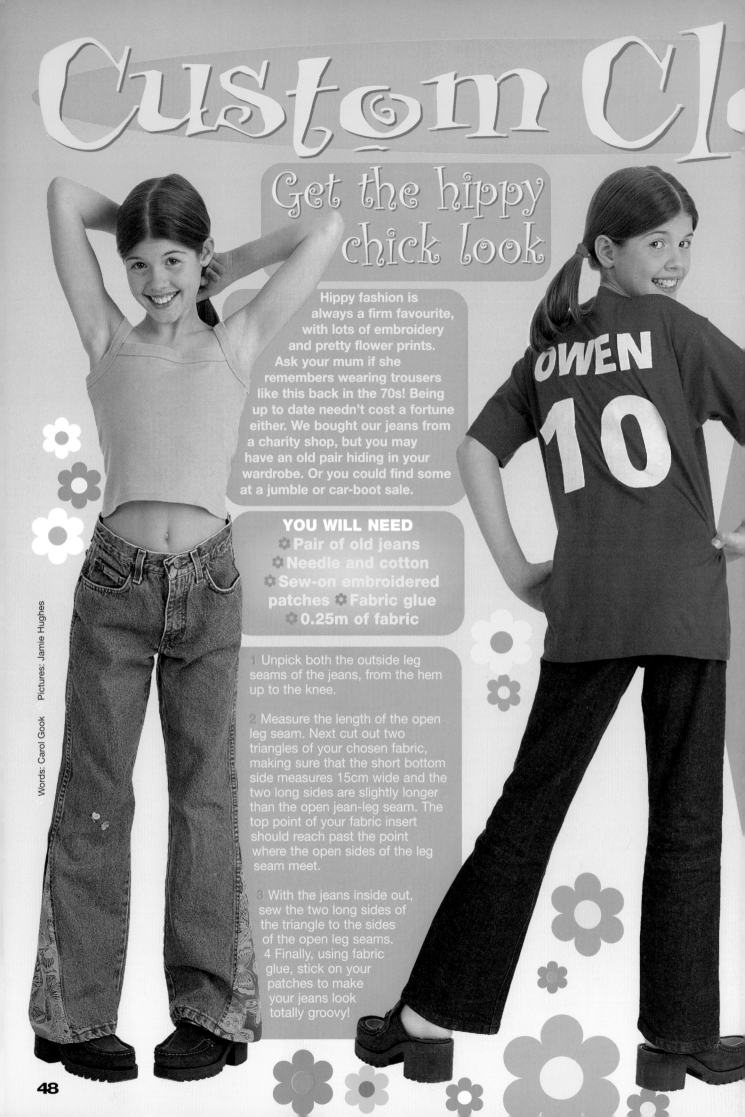

Custom Cl...

Get the hippy chick look

Hippy fashion is always a firm favourite, with lots of embroidery and pretty flower prints. Ask your mum if she remembers wearing trousers like this back in the 70s! Being up to date needn't cost a fortune either. We bought our jeans from a charity shop, but you may have an old pair hiding in your wardrobe. Or you could find some at a jumble or car-boot sale.

YOU WILL NEED
✿ Pair of old jeans
✿ Needle and cotton
✿ Sew-on embroidered patches ✿ Fabric glue
✿ 0.25m of fabric

1 Unpick both the outside leg seams of the jeans, from the hem up to the knee.

2 Measure the length of the open leg seam. Next cut out two triangles of your chosen fabric, making sure that the short bottom side measures 15cm wide and the two long sides are slightly longer than the open jean-leg seam. The top point of your fabric insert should reach past the point where the open sides of the leg seam meet.

3 With the jeans inside out, sew the two long sides of the triangle to the sides of the open leg seams.
4 Finally, using fabric glue, stick on your patches to make your jeans look totally groovy!

OWEN 10

Words: Carol Gook ✿ Pictures: Jamie Hughes

Be a sporty supergirl

We all love football here at *Girl Talk,* and we know you do, too. Official team shirts cost a lot of money, but you can make this fab footie top for a fraction of the price. You can even customise it with your favourite team member's name and number!

YOU WILL NEED
✿ **Red (or your team's colour) T-shirt** ✿ **White felt fabric** ✿ **Glue** ✿ **Pencil** ✿ **Tracing paper** ✿ **Front pages from old newspaper**

1 It will be easier to make the name and number of your favourite football star if you can use a computer. Create a document and type in your player's name and number. Select a big point size – around 72 – for the letters. (Ask an adult if you need help.) Another way is to cut out big letters from headlines in old newspapers. You may need to use the photocopier to make them bigger. We chose Michael Owen and his number, ten.

2 Place the cutout letters on the felt and draw round them. Then cut them out.

3 Arrange them on the back of the T-shirt. Next, carefully pick them up one at a time and stick them down in the right place.

4 Draw a big figure ten on a sheet of paper and cut out the numbers.

5 Place the numbers on the back of the shirt.

6 Stick them down one at a time in the right place. Now you're ready to go for goal!

Fun and fluffy

Take one old T-shirt, add some lovely marabou trim, put glitter on your face, some cool clips in your hair and you're ready to party!

YOU WILL NEED
✿ **Needle and cotton**
✿ **1m marabou trim**
✿ **White T-shirt**

1 Sew marabou trim all around the neck of the T-shirt, making sure that you pass the needle through the cord in the middle of the marabou.

2 When you get to the end cut it carefully and sew it down.

3 Repeat this around the cuff of each sleeve to see your old T-shirt transformed into a cool new top.

JESSICA THE TV STAR

JESSICA THE TV STAR

Todd was fooled into thinking Jessica was Elizabeth

You did the rehearsal for the TV show on Tuesday, Elizabeth!

Todd, I was sick and stayed in bed all day.

Then it was Jessica! I really wanted you to be on TV with me, Elizabeth.

Where is Jessica? I want a word with her.

There you are! Now, what's the big idea?

Come on, kids! Let's get moving here.

Let's do what the director says!

Now, just remember what we did yesterday.

But I wasn't…

When the phone rings, Todd is going to answer it.

Lewis residence. Mickey speaking.

And… cut! You did a great job, kids.

You knew Todd wanted me to be in the programme and you weren't going to tell me!

Well, I'm angry with Todd. He said I was bossy!

It was just a joke – pretending to be you at school, Liz. And then I couldn't stop.

I forgive you.

I think you've learnt your lesson.

Hey, there you all are. How did it go?

Call of the wild

Orphan Elephant Fostering Certificate

UASO

is being fostered by

Girl Talk Magazine

This young orphan elephant is in Kenya under the expert care of Daphne Sheldrick.

You are helping to ensure the continued good health and happiness of this orphan.

Your support will help to pay for the supplies and care that is needed both in Tsavo and also at Daphne Sheldrick's nursery in Nairobi where the orphans are taken when they are first found.

19th January 1999

This fostering commences for one year from this date

Bill Jordan
Care for the Wild International

Orphan Elephant Fostering Certificate

EMILY

is being fostered by

Girl Talk Magazine

This young orphan elephant is in Kenya under the expert care of Daphne Sheldrick.

You are helping to ensure the continued good health and happiness of this orphan.

Your support will help to pay for the supplies and care that is needed both in Tsavo and also at Daphne Sheldrick's nursery in Nairobi where the orphans are taken when they are first found.

19th January 1999

This fostering commences for one year from this date

Bill Jordan
Chairman, Care for the Wild International
Registered Charity Number 288802

Remember: Elephants never forget - especially wh...

Even if you can't see a tiger in the wild, you can still stay in touch with nature. Fostering is a great way to get involved with some of the planet's most beautiful, and most threatened, creatures

Emily and Uaso

Becoming a foster parent is great way to protect endangered animals. *Girl Talk* fosters two elephants, Emily and Uaso, who live at the Tsavo National Park in Kenya. These two orphans are cared for by the charity Care for the Wild International and have now become great friends. Here are some ideas how you can sponsor an animal yourself.

Grrreat!

This orphaned tiger was rescued from a dealer by the Royal Forestry Department of Bangkok. Sadly, without their mothers' upbringing, orphaned tigers can't survive in the wild. As there were few facilities in Thailand for tigers Care for the Wild created two natural-habitat sanctuaries called Tiger Mountain I and II. These are the biggest animal enclosures of their kind in the world. They have everything tigers need to feel at home – shady trees, mountainous boulders, bamboo groves, even a waterfall and pool to swim in. The number of wild tigers has shrunk dramatically this century, but you can help preserve the species worldwide by adopting one. Care for the Wild send out a cool gift pack when you foster an orphan tiger. Write to: **Care for the Wild International,** 1 Ashfolds, Horsham Road, Rusper, West Sussex, RH12 4QX.

Horse sense

Have you ever wanted your own pony? Well, why not adopt one? Redwings Horse Sanctuary, located across five farms in the Norfolk countryside, cares for unwanted horses, ponies and donkeys. They currently look after a thousand animals! There are caring staff and resident vets on call at all times. For only £6 a year supporters can adopt one of the rescued horses, ponies or donkeys. In return you receive an adoption certificate, a twice-yearly report and a photograph of your horse or pony. Write to: **Redwings Horse Sanctuary,** Hall Lane, Frettenham, Norwich, NR12 7RW, or call (01603) 737432 for details.

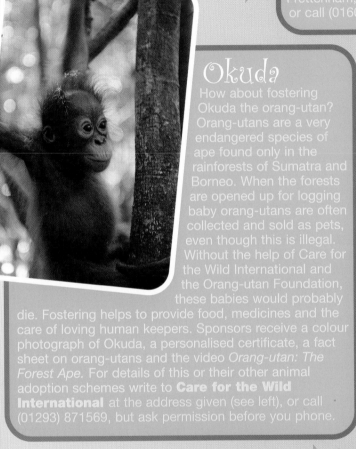

Okuda

How about fostering Okuda the orang-utan? Orang-utans are a very endangered species of ape found only in the rainforests of Sumatra and Borneo. When the forests are opened up for logging baby orang-utans are often collected and sold as pets, even though this is illegal. Without the help of Care for the Wild International and the Orang-utan Foundation, these babies would probably die. Fostering helps to provide food, medicines and the care of loving human keepers. Sponsors receive a colour photograph of Okuda, a personalised certificate, a fact sheet on orang-utans and the video *Orang-utan: The Forest Ape*. For details of this or their other animal adoption schemes write to **Care for the Wild International** at the address given (see left), or call (01293) 871569, but ask permission before you phone.

What a life!

The Dartmoor Otter Sanctuary is home to 13 otters. The sanctuary cares for sick and injured otters, unwanted pets or other otters bred in captivity, which could not survive in the wild. In the wild, otters usually live for six to seven years, but there are some very happy 17-year-olds living in the comfort of the sanctuary's man-made holts (or dens). If you would like more information about sponsoring an otter, write to: **Dartmoor Otter Sanctuary,** Buckfastleigh, Devon, TQ11 0DZ or call (01364) 642916, but check with whoever pays the bills first.

Save the whale

The Whale and Dolphin Conservation Society (WDCS) is the largest charity of its kind in the world. Dedicated to the conservation, welfare and appreciation of whales, dolphins and porpoises, WDCS now has over 70,000 members and supporters who contribute to its work to ensure a secure future for these beautiful creatures. The eight recognised species of whales, dolphins and porpoises include the largest animal on earth and the deepest-diving mammal. They also include some of our most endangered species. By adopting a dolphin you can help all whales and dolphins. As a sponsor you receive an adoption certificate with biographical information and a picture of your dolphin, a window sticker plus the Echo newsletter every six months. For more details write to: **Whale and Dolphin Conservation Society,** FREEPOST (SN 863), Bath, BA1 2XF, or call (01225) 334511, but ask before you phone.

Nasrin's Egypt

"Loads of old pots," groaned Kirsty. "Boring!"

Kirsty was beginning to get on Nasrin's nerves. She was Nasrin's best friend but sometimes she could be a right pain. Nasrin was enjoying their class visit to the museum. Linda, the museum guide, had given them each a clipboard and a set of worksheets. "You'll find the answers to the questions by looking carefully at the different displays," Linda had said to them.

Mrs Henderson, their teacher had told the children they could work in pairs. "I didn't think we'd actually have to work," grumbled Kirsty. The girls were in a small room that was full of pots in glass cases. Unlike the other rooms in the museum it didn't seem to lead anywhere else. There was an archway at the end of the room but it had a rope across it. Behind the rope was a big display board with a notice pinned to it. "Not open to the public," read Kirsty. "This room's a dead end, anyway. Let's go back."

That's not fair!

"There's a question about Roman pottery on the worksheet," said Nasrin. "We might find the answer in here."

Kirsty groaned. "Who cares about a stupid worksheet," she said. Nasrin was beginning to wish she had worked with someone else. Kirsty hadn't stopped moaning all morning. "What's Mrs Henderson going to say if you haven't filled in your worksheet?" she asked.

Kirsty shrugged. "I'll just copy your answers," she said.

"That's not fair!" Nasrin was really fed up with Kirsty now. "Why should I do all the work? You're always copying me."

"No, I'm not," said Kirsty, her face going very red.

"You are," said Nasrin. "Mrs Henderson is always telling you not to copy."

"Well, what's Mrs Henderson going to say about this then?" shouted

> When Kirsten threw Nasrin's work away the two girls couldn't believe what it led them into

Kirsty. She snatched Nasrin's clipboard and threw it over the rope. Nasrin gasped as it skidded under the legs of the display board and into the closed-off room. Both the girls were silent. Nasrin was used to Kirsty's hot temper but couldn't believe what she had done this time. It looked like Kirsty couldn't believe it either. "I'm sorry, Nasrin," she said. "I'll go in and get it back for you."

"I don't think…" began Nasrin. But Kirsty had already climbed over the rope and was squeezing into the gap at the side of the display board. Suddenly Nasrin voice in the room behind her. What should she do? The teacher was bound to ask where Kirsty was and she didn't want to get her into trouble. Quickly she jumped over the rope and went after Kirsty.

Where are we?

Behind the display boards were some long heavy curtains. Nasrin pushed her way through and found herself in a new and strange world. "Kirsty?" she hissed.

Kirsty was standing staring. "Where are we?" she whispered back.

They were in a huge dimly lit room. The walls seemed to be made of big blocks of stone. There was a smell of sweet perfume and the soft sound of pipes and tinkling bells.

"Look," said Kirsty, pointing to one of the walls. It was so dark in the room it took Nasrin a while to see what Kirsty was pointing at. Then her eyes got used to the darkness and she saw one of the walls was decorated with paintings. The pictures looked familiar. There were people with animal heads carrying golden jars, and strange writing like pictures.

"Do you think we're in an Egyptian pyramid?" whispered Kirsty.

"It's only a display," said Nasrin. But was it? It felt so real and spooky. None of the other displays in the museum were a bit like this. What if they really had walked into another world – like the children who found Narnia on the other side of a wardrobe?

"Oh no!" hissed Kirsty, grabbing Nasrin's arm. "A mummy!"

Nasrin looked where Kirsty was pointing. She could just make out a pale bandaged figure. It was in a big case leaning upright against the wall. Nasrin remembered an old film she had watched with her brother. The mummy had come to life and walked straight out of its case. But that was a stupid old film and this was just…

Let's get out!

Suddenly there was a loud clashing noise. Nasrin nearly jumped out of her skin. She was sure she could hear Kirsty's heart bumping, too. One of the big stones in the wall rose up to make a doorway. A man dressed in golden robes started walking out. He looked just like the pictures Nasrin had seen of ancient Egyptians and he was carrying a dagger.

"Let's get out of here!" screamed Kirsty.

Nasrin began screaming, too, as they rushed for the curtains.

"What the..?" Nasrin heard the man shouting.

Suddenly someone was holding onto her arms and all the lights went on. Nasrin looked up into Mrs Henderson's face. She was looking very cross. Linda, the museum guide, was standing by the light switch. Nasrin thought she looked pretty cross, too.

"What are you girls doing in here?" snapped Mrs Henderson. "And what's all this awful squealing about?"

While Kirsty tried to explain, Nasrin looked around. Now the lights were on she couldn't see why they had

Illustration: Flora Daneman

ian experience

A story by Katie Bright

been so scared. She could see that the stone walls and the mummy weren't real.

The Egyptian man began to laugh. "I think our Egyptian Experience is going to be a huge success," he said. Then Linda started laughing and even Mrs Henderson smiled.

Linda explained that the room was closed because they were preparing for a new display called the Egyptian Experience. "Mike here is an actor," she said. "The actors are going to play the part of the Egyptian priests and pharaohs. We want it to look and feel just like ancient Egypt."

"It felt real, all right," grinned Kirsty.

"You shouldn't have come in, though," insisted Mrs Henderson. "What if the museum had been doing repairs? It could have been dangerous."

Both Nasrin and Kirsty said that they were sorry.

"Aren't we doing ancient Egypt next term?" asked Nasrin as they followed Mrs Henderson out. "Could we come to the Egyptian Experience?"

"Only if you show me you can behave yourselves," said Mrs Henderson.

"We will," the girls chorused.

Kirsty nudged Nasrin. "I'll never say that museums are boring again," she whispered. ✿

We've put together this giant quiz to see how much you know about everything we have done or learnt about our world during the past millennium. So get your mates together and see who gets the highest score when you pit your wits against the…

BUMPER GENERAL KNOWLEDGE QUIZ

Girl TALK

BOOKS

1 Who wrote *Alice's Adventures in Wonderland*?
2 What was the name of the headmistress in Roald Dahl's *Matilda*?
3 What is the bestselling book of all time?
4 Who wrote a book about the adventures of a sheep-pig?
5 In which series of books would you find Gemma, Lauren, Anya, Carli and Sunita?
6 Which part is the spine of a book?
7 In which series of books does a dummy come to life?
8 Who wrote *Gulliver's Travels*?
9 How many plays did William Shakespeare write?
10 What is an epic?
11 Who wrote *Robinson Crusoe*?
12 What do you call a book with a soft cover?

GEOGRAPHY

1 Name the capital of Mexico.
2 What is the highest mountain in the world?
3 Where are the biggest sand dunes in the world?
4 In which country would you find the Grand Canyon?
5 How many stars are there on the American flag?
6 Where would you find the Empire State Building?
7 Which country is known as the Emerald Isle?
8 Which country produces the most tea?
9 Where is the busiest airport in the world?
10 What is the highest waterfall in the world?
11 What is the smallest city in the world?
12 Which large river runs through London?

HISTORY

1 Which Scottish engineer is famous for inventing a television system?
2 Who was the first female British prime minister?
3 Who was the first man to walk on the moon?
4 What was Albert Einstein famous for?
5 Who invented the telephone?
6 Who was the first President of America?
7 Which explorer is famous for discovering America?
8 Who was the first explorer to reach the south pole?
9 In what year was the United Nations founded?
10 Who was Tutankhamen?
11 When was the Battle of Hastings?
12 Who were the Vikings?

✿ Words: Nora Kearns

SPORT

1 In 1970 which football team became the first to win the World Cup three times?
2 In which country did the sport of ice hockey originate?
3 Where is the world's largest covered sports stadium?
4 In which sport would you perform a triple toe loop?
5 What is the name of Manchester United's home ground?
6 In which sport do you score an ace?
7 In which sport would you hit a shuttlecock?
8 In which sport would you perform a butterfly?
9 How many rings are there in the Olympic symbol?
10 In which sport would you use a foil?
11 Name two sports which use an oval football.
12 In which sport would you perform a back flip?

SCIENCE

1 What is lava?
2 What do the letters C and F stand for on a thermometer?
3 At what temperature does water freeze?
4 What does the chemical symbol H_2O stand for?
5 What do scientists use to measure rainfall?
6 What is the largest organ in the human body?
7 What is the name given to the study of earthquakes?
8 What is the hardest mineral?
9 What is the softest mineral?
10 What is the name given to water vapour that has turned to ice?
11 What is a glacier?
12 What is an oasis?

NATURAL HISTORY

1 What would you look at to find out a horse's age?
2 What was the largest dinosaur?
3 Name the largest living bird?
4 What is the fastest mammal on land?
5 How many legs does a spider have?
6 What are amphibians?

7 What is the longest snake in the world?
8 What is the deadliest snake?
9 Which are the biggest cats?
10 What kind of creature are crabs, lobsters and oysters?
11 What is the largest living land mammal?
12 What does a caterpillar become?

Answers

Books – 1 Lewis Carroll 2 Miss Trunchbull 3 The Bible 4 Dick King-Smith 5 Girl Talk Best Friends series 6 The back of the cover, where the pages are glued or stitched together 7 Goosebumps 8 Jonathan Swift 9 37 10 A long poem which tells a story 11 Daniel Defoe 12 A paperback

Geography – 1 Mexico City 2 Mount Everest 3 Sahara Desert, North Africa 4 North America 5 50 6 New York 7 Ireland 8 India 9 O'Hare in Chicago, USA 10 Salto Angel (Angel Falls), Venezuela 11 The Vatican City 12 River Thames

History – 1 John Logie Baird 2 Margaret Thatcher 3 Neil Armstrong 4 He was famous for formulating the theory of relativity 5 Alexander Graham Bell 6 George Washington 7 Christopher Columbus 8 Roald Amundsen 9 1945 10 An Egyptian king 11 1066 12 Sailors from Scandinavia who terrorised Europe between the seventh and tenth centuries

Sport – 1 Brazil 2 Canada 3 Aztec Stadium, Mexico City 4 Ice skating 5 Old Trafford 6 Tennis 7 Badminton 8 Swimming 9 Five 10 Fencing 11 American football and rugby 12 Gymnastics

Science – 1 Hot molten rock from within the earth's crust 2 Celsius and Fahrenheit 3 0°C (32°F) 4 Water 5 A rain gauge 6 The liver 7 Seismology 8 Diamond 9 Talc, which consists of magnesium silicate 10 Snow 11 A large mass of ice found in the polar regions 12 A fertile area surrounded by desert

Natural history – 1 Its teeth 2 Brachiosaurus 3 Ostrich 4 Cheetah 5 Eight 6 Any cold-blooded vertebrate of the class Amphibia, typically living on land but breeding in water. These include toads, frogs, newts and salamanders. 7 Reticulated python 8 The Australian sea snake Hydrophis belcheri 9 Tigers 10 Crustaceans 11 African elephant 12 A butterfly

Photo: David White